Mandy FOR GIRLS 1988

PICTURE-STORIES

THINGS TO MAKE AND DO

STORIES TO READ

Printed and Published in Great Britain by D. C. THOMSON & CO., LTD., 185 Fleet Street, London EC4A 2HS. © D. C. THOMSON & CO., LTD., 1987.
ISBN 0-85116-389-0

£2.80

WATCH WHAT YOU TELL TINA!

THE Wilsons were a happy, if hard-up family. Eleven-year-old Carol was the eldest of five children, baby Colin was the youngest — and the middle one, seven-year-old Tina, was a real little character!

Smile, please —

Trust Tina to be out in the front of the picture!

One afternoon —

What are you making for tea tonight, Mum? I'm starving!

Nothing much, Tina — you'll just have to have a run round the table tonight, instead!

We're always short of food, with Dad out of work.

Here's Dad home — he's been job-hunting, as usual.

Hi, love! What's that racket in the living-room? It sounds like a baby elephant!

Oops — sorry, Dad!

5

7

8

10

Attention, parents — has your baby been swopped for a bike? If so, we have him safe and sound, in our van.

Oh, Carol — thank goodness.

The van stopped.

We passed you at just the right time! When our daughter Maxine arrived home with a baby, we thought we'd use one of my firm's vans to do some detective work.

You'll be glad to have him back.

You can say that again!

Maxine's bike is at our house, if you'd like to come in for it.

Thanks for acting so promptly, Mr Carter. The truth is, our Tina thought we'd have one less mouth to feed without Colin. I lost my job as an electrical engineer months ago — and so far, I can't get another.

Really? Maybe I can help.

Two days later —

I've done it, everyone — I've got a job with Carter Electrics, starting Monday.

That's great, dear!

Yeah, it's magic! Can I have a bike soon, Dad?

Tina — honestly!

But Dad bought them all bikes!

Everything's worked out great, thanks to the baby-and-bike swop! But more than ever now — we're watching what we tell Tina!

THE END

13

15

16

Sue took a shot herself —

Oh, dear — he stopped it.

Oh, no! Sue should have passed to *ME*!

Wanderers took the lead, with a goal just before half-time.

How's the head, Daphne? That was a nasty bump.

I'm all right, Kenny. I think you're playing wonderfully!

Huh! I wonder if he'd be so concerned if *I* got injured?

So, in the second half, Sue tried her luck —

AAAGH! My leg —

Don't come the play-acting with me, missy! You're not hurt — get up and play on!

Well! My leg could be *BROKEN* — but Kenny just ignores me!

Still trailing 1-0, time was running out for United — and for Sue.

If we don't get an equaliser, we'll be out of the Cup — then I'll be out of the team, and away from Kenny!

17

18

The End

Once Upon A Time

FAIRY Godmother Maud is on her way, girls — to tell you the "truth" about a fairy story. She should have been here earlier but — oh, here she comes now!

EEEEEYAHHHH!

Dratted spell! I said, "Soar in style and gently land" — not "Sore in a pile, on mucky sand"! Oh — hello, you lot!

Now for another startling revelation in the world of fairy stories. Today it's Little Red Riding Hood. Little! That's a laugh! Read on, girls—

FAIRY DUST

"Little" Red Riding Hood was nearly six feet tall, and a very nice lass.

Take this home-made loaf and jar of jam to your Grandma, dear. She hasn't been too well lately.

Yes, Mother dear.

A little later, Little Red Riding Hood was loping her way through the woods.

I hope Grandma's feeling better. She gets so upset about things.

Soon—

Oh, dear — oh, my! Here comes someone now. Maybe she knows the way out of this wood. My sense of direction is terrible.

Excuse me, miss — but could you show me the way out of this wood? I'm lost.

I'm not supposed to talk to strangers, Mr Wolf. Mother said so.

20

While Little Red Riding Hood picked a bunch of flowers for her Grandma, the wolf went off — and promptly got lost again.

Moments later—

21

Pie's Promise

JENNY MANNING was on a visit to York Castle Museum, with a party from her school.

Now, we'll carry on with our tour of the Victorian street area—

The coach door's been left open! I'm tired — no one will notice if I take a rest in here.

Mmmm — quite comfortable. I'll pretend I'm a grand lady, riding through the streets of York to my mansion on the hill. Oh, dear — my servants haven't patched this seat too well!

J.W. NELSON SADDLER

Suddenly, the coach seemed to rock violently.

Hey! Stop it! Let me out of here! YOU'RE doing this, Olive Clark! I'll tell Miss Granger!

24

But when Jenny got out of the coach—

Fog! This is weird — I can hardly see anything. I'd better catch up with the others quickly. I'll ask at the nearest shop if they came this way.

Have my school friends been in here, please? I've lost them. They are all about my age, and carrying lunch bags like this.

I'm sorry, miss. I've had no such customers in here today.

The fog had lifted—

I — I don't believe it — hooped skirts, bonnets, tall hats and tail coats. This isn't the museum — it's *REAL!* I'm frightened! I — I've *GOT* to get back to the museum.

Suddenly—

Get out of the way! Why don't you look where you're going?

Badly shaken, Jenny felt sick and lost.

I'm not even in my own time, never mind the right place! Whatever am I going to do?

Just then—

Stop, thief! Catch that brat!

That poor boy — his eyes are full of terror, almost *PLEADING* with me to help him!

And so—

That's stopped him! But now I'd better clear out!

Jenny quickly ran up a nearby alleyway.

Phew! I think I've managed to dodge him. But there's someone here — in the shadows!

Thanks, miss. You saved me for sure. Old Fatty would have caught me if you hadn't tripped him up. My name's Pie.

I'm Jenny Manning. Look, Pie — I'm lost. Will you take me to the museum?

He doesn't know what I'm talking about! There *ISN'T* a museum — and I'm trapped here in Victorian York! But if I stay with Pie, perhaps I'll find a way back somehow.

Pie led Jenny through a maze of alleyways.

Why were you being chased — and where did you get your strange name? Is it short for something?

Old Fatty was chasing me because I pinched some stale bread from his shop. And I'm called Pie cos I *LIKE* pies!

26

Pie's "home" was the rooftop of a large butcher's shop.

Is this really where you live?

You'll get used to it. Wrap this round you — it gets very cold at night. The family will be here soon.

And, later—

This is my family — Sarah, Maggie and young Biff.

Who's the lady, Pie?

This is Jenny Manning, Sarah. She saved me from Old Fatty. Here, Jenny — have some bread.

No, thanks — I've got my own food.

When Jenny opened her lunch box, the ragged children gazed wide-eyed at the contents.

POTATO CRISPS
CHOC

Poor things — they're like skeletons! I bet they haven't seen this much food for one meal in their lives. That little blind Maggie — she can only smell the food, but her mouth's watering.

27

Here you are — I'm not very hungry. Those are potato crisps, and inside those coloured papers are chocolate biscuits. Go on, they're very good — eat them.

Soon, every scrap was eaten.

That was a real treat. Thanks, Miss Jenny.

That's all right, Maggie. I'm glad you liked it.

During the cold dark night—

I'm freezing, and so uncomfortable. I don't know how the others can manage to sleep. I've *GOT* to get back to my own time! I can't live like this. Oh, why did I ever get into that coach?

Next day, Jenny learned how to beg for her breakfast —

Spare a penny, sir, for the little ones.

Just look at these well-dressed people! They see starving ragged children — and they just don't care!

During the morning, Jenny saw how the beggar children earned money to buy a meagre supply of food—

— holding horses —

— carrying shopping —

— sweeping street crossings.

"We've done well today. I'll be able to save a little money towards clothes and things. Jenny, I believe you've brought us luck!"

"I'm so hungry — I'm even eating this stale bread, and rotten fruit and vegetables. Can this be how they live EVERY day? How do they survive? There MUST be a way to help them!"

"Miss Jenny, you dress funny and you talk funny — not like us. Tell us where you come from. Are you a rich lady from a big house, who's got lost?"

Jenny tried to explain her fantastic story—

"This is the museum — the place I came from. I feel that I must find it, before I can get back to my own time."

"This is a strange pen, which writes without a bottle of ink. Can it be true what you told us, about your world of the future?"

"I wish I could take you all home with me. You'd have a much happier life — a house to live in, beds with clean sheets, plenty of food."

29

Are there lots of children like me, where you came from, Jenny?

Yes, there are orphans, Biff — but they are looked after by kind people.

They live in *REAL* houses — with beds, and clean sheets and lots of food?

One day, Jenny — *I'M* going to have a house and everything, just like you said. I'm going to work and save till I can give these little 'uns all the things rich people have. I *WILL* do it for them — and that's a *PROMISE!*

Next day—

Jenny, I'll try an' help you go back to your own time.

Thanks. And Pie — I know you'll keep your promise about the children, somehow.

Just then, as they came round a corner—

Leave that bag alone, you rogue!

Look — that gentleman is being robbed!

Hold on, sir — I'll stop him!

Thanks to Pie and Jenny, the thief was soon under arrest—

Are you all right?

Yes — thanks to you and your friend, my dear. I was on my way to the bank, and stopped while my coachman collected a parcel. Then that rascal attacked me.

That patch! Why — this is the same coach as in the museum!

Suddenly, everything seemed to rock—

Wait — I haven't said goodbye—

Slowly, very slowly, Jenny became aware of voices—

It — it's Miss Granger's voice!

Feeling strangely light-headed, but perfectly fit, Jenny slid silently from the coach and joined the school party.

This portrait is of a most remarkable man. Mr Pie Manning was an orphan. He grew up in the last century in the city streets, caring for his little brother and sisters. At the early age of twelve, he became a clerk at a bank.

Pie Manning worked very hard over the years, to better himself. The owner of the bank took a special interest in him. Eventually he bought a house, and so founded the Manning Orphanage for Homeless Children.

And he gave them beds with clean sheets, and lots of lovely food.

What was that, Jenny? Manning — he wasn't an ancestor of yours, was he?

No, Miss Granger.

Just a friend, who borrowed my name!

Behind the whiskers and serious expression, Jenny could easily recognise Pie — by the determined look in his eyes.

You did it, Pie! You *KEPT* your promise!

The End

To Love and Cherish

JILL kicked the stone into the gutter, and then walked across to the back gate. Standing with her hand on the latch, she drew a deep breath, and then let it out very slowly. By now Cherie would have been at the door to meet her, flitting soundlessly round her feet, arching her back, rubbing herself against Jill's knee, looking up at her with round, dark blue eyes.

Oh, Cherie!

Tears rolled down Jill's cheeks, and she brushed them away impatiently with her fingers. It wasn't any use. Nothing could bring Cherie back.

She opened the gate, and walked slowly up the path. Cherie's red ball had disappeared from the square of green lawn, and so had the old grey jumper which Jill had folded and stuffed, to make a little cushion for her to sit on, on the square of crazy paving by the pink hydrangea.

Even the dish with her name on it had gone from the steps. Jill remembered stencilling CHERIE in thick, wavy black letters when she'd been about seven or so. It had taken her ages.

Now, no sign remained that a beautiful seal-point Siamese cat had ever lived at 7 Court Avenue. Jill saw her mother watching from the kitchen window, and lifted her hand in a half-hearted wave.

"I thought it was best, love," Mum said as Jill draped her duffle coat over the back of the chair. "Otherwise everything would keep reminding you."

"It's okay, Mum," Jill mumbled, trying to keep her voice steady. Trouble was, everywhere she looked she seemed to see Cherie.

"She *was* getting on," her mother went on, threading the teacloth through anxious fingers as she spoke. "Nearly eleven, remember. That's a fair age for a cat, you know."

"I know," Jill said. Funny, it being old for an animal and yet young for a person, she thought. I was only a month older than Cherie, after all.

"We could always have another," her mother said. "If you wanted."

"I don't," Jill said firmly. "Honest, Mum. I just couldn't." She swallowed the lump in her throat and turned away.

Two days, six hours, since Cherie had died. And Jill hadn't stopped thinking about her, not once. She never would. Jill ate her tea, and then went slowly upstairs to her room. She had masses of homework to do, but she knew she'd never concentrate. She went across to the window, staring down into next-door's garden. Bev would have understood, if she'd been here. If she and her family hadn't moved last month. Listlessly, Jill turned to the maths book.

"I don't know, Jill," Miss Makins grumbled next day. "You used to be good at arithmetic. These are all wrong, every single one. You must try and pull yourself together or you'll never keep your position in class."

Blushing furiously, Jill took back her work. Nothing seemed to be going right lately. Nothing. And the rest of that week seemed to drag by on leaden feet. Even her mother appeared to be losing patience when Jill misheard the shopping list for the third time.

"Flour, sugar and sultanas," her mother said in exasperation. "And do try to remember it's self-raising, not plain. You'd better go now, too, or you'll miss the bus."

And that was exactly what happened, on top of everything else. Jill reached the corner just as the familiar blue and cream vehicle drew away from the stop.

Bother, she thought. And Hallows Way is about the most boring road ever. It just stretches on and on for what seems like miles.

Only this morning, she was wrong.

For once, something *was* going on — a snarling, brawling fight!

Halfway down, where the houses petered out into a clutch of garages, a large excited dog had cornered something. And that something set up such a shrieking frightened protest, that Jill knew it could only be one animal.

A cat.

Crossing the courtyard, braving the dog, she saw a small grey tabby, fur bristling, claws stretched, trembling with fear.

She caught hold of the dog's collar. He turned his head, indignant, and tried to sink his teeth into her wrist. As she snatched her hand away, a shrill whistling sounded somewhere in a back garden. Immediately, the dog became alert, listening. Jill seized her chance and gathered up the small cat, tucking her inside her duffle. The dog hesitated, and Jill gave him a push. The whistle came again, and the dog made up his mind. He dashed away to his unseen owner.

The tabby looked up at Jill and began to purr, kneading her claws against her woolly jumper. Jill felt her heart lurch. If she closed her eyes, it might almost have been Cherie.

No, she said to herself. No. I'm going to find your owner. Can't just leave you here, in case that dog comes back.

She knocked on several doors. No one had ever seen the little cat before. Two or three said they were quite sure she didn't live anywhere round Hallows Way.

Finally, Jill took her home.

"I'll put an ad in the newsagent's window, love," her mother promised.

Two days later, with the little tabby waiting for her each afternoon on her return from school, Jill began to hope against hope that no one *would* claim her.

Because Shona, as Jill called her, had crept into her heart and was beginning to warm her, to fill the awful aching void Cherie had left. Little by little, Jill felt she was coming alive again.

And then the blow fell.

On the Thursday there was no Shona, and Mum told her a Mrs Quentin had come for the tabby.

Jill stared miserably at her mother.

"She left her address," her mother went on. "She says she'd like to reward you."

"I don't want anything," Jill said, choking back the tears.

It just didn't seem fair. No Cherie, then no Shona. It was all too much. She hadn't even had a chance to say goodbye to the little tabby.

"Well, why don't you just go and see for yourself that Shona's really happy," her

mother suggested. "Mrs Quentin was so nice — she'd understand."

Jill didn't know if she could bear it. But at school next day, thinking about it at break, she knew she'd go. Even if Shona had already forgotten her. She'd go next week, at half-term.

But Shona hadn't forgotten.

She leapt on to Jill's lap, purring and kneading her claws.

"I can see she was in good hands," Mrs Quentin smiled. She was a plumpish, pretty woman, with soft eyes. "And now, you've really got to accept something that I'd very much like you to have."

"Oh no, please — " Jill began.

"In a few weeks, if you don't mind waiting," Mrs Quentin said firmly.

Jill stared at her in bewilderment.

"Come and see," Mrs Quentin said, stretching out a hand.

Shona ran ahead of them.

Mrs Quentin opened the door of a cupboard in the kitchen.

"There," she whispered, pointing to a cardboard box. "Two days old, would you believe? Aren't they lovely?"

And Jill peered in at three of the most beautiful kittens she'd even seen. One black, one sandy — and one the image of Shona. As she looked, entranced, Shona began running a warm pink tongue over the face of the tiny tabby.

"Oh!" Jill breathed. "Oh, they're so alike. Like — well, mother and daughter!" And then, tremulous, unable to believe, "Is — is that one for me? Really and truly?"

"Really and truly," Mrs Quentin said.

Jill put out a trembling finger, and touched the little animal's ear. Somehow, the wee kitten was Cherie and Shona all rolled up into one warm bundle of love. And suddenly, thinking of them both, the right name came to her mind immediately.

"I shall call her Cherish," she whispered. "Because that's exactly what I shall do. Love and cherish her for ever and ever."

And somehow, looking down, she knew it was going to be the start of a relationship as happy and long as it had been with Cherie. And wherever Cherie was, Jill knew she'd approve. Just as Shona did, as she stared unblinkingly back into Jill's eyes, as if knowing her daughter was going to the best home in the whole world, to the luckiest girl alive!

THE END

Polly's PERFECT Mum

POLLY GORDON persuaded her mother to enter for a "Perfect Mum" competition. That was a big mistake — because Mum Gordon won, and life became *VERY* difficult for the rest of the family. Polly's Perfect Mum was determined to turn Dad, Polly and Sam into a "perfect" family! One morning —

It's raining cats and dogs, kids! What horrible weather for a public holiday — I won't get any gardening done today!

Come off it, Dad — you're not as keen on gardening as all that!

Well, Polly — there *ARE* good programmes on TV all day — cartoons, comedy shows, and a big film at night —

Great! It's just the day for watching telly.

TODAY'S *TELEVISION*

But, after lunch —

Hey — what are you doing, Kate?

THE PERFECT MUM

Switching off! Perfect Mums don't let their families laze around watching rubbish all day!

What you lot need is some culture! If you'd read the "What's on" bit in the paper, instead of the TV programmes, you'd have noticed that the art gallery is open today — and THAT'S where we're all going this afternoon!

But I don't like art galleries —

Nor me, Mum.

Er — I'll stay home and look after Butch! I mean, they won't let dogs in the art gallery, will they?

No — but we'll drop Butch off at Gran Gordon's on the way. I don't want you to miss an interesting afternoon, Polly.

Interesting? You're joking, Kate! And don't you think it's a bit wet for going out? We might catch nasty colds —

No excuses! We'll be going by car, and the art gallery is one of the warmest places I know!

And so, Butch was taken to Gran's —

Here he is, Gran —

Butch won't get to romp about in Gran's tiny flat. He's in for a miserable afternoon, too — like us!

Then, at the art gallery —

What a wonderful painting! You can almost hear the sea, rushing on to the shore —

Psst! If I had my way, we'd be rushing out of here, and home to the telly.

Too true, Dad.

The colours in this still life are so realistic —

I'd rather see the colour on our telly, kids.

Yeah — yawn — I wonder what we're missing?

At long last —

Phew — thank goodness that's over! Let's get home now — the car's this way —

Not so fast, you lot!

We've the museum to do yet! It's just round the corner —

ANOTHER boring place! You're really making us suffer, Kate!

Here we are! This is far better for you than sitting glued to the telly. I'm out to improve my family's minds.

Oh, is that what you call it?

Aren't old things fascinating?

The old things we like best are old films on the box!

A boring hour later —

Right, let's pick up Butch, and get home for a quick tea. Then we can settle down to watch the big film.

But Mum Gordon had other plans —

Stop here, Jim! I want to get something out of the library.

PUBLIC LIBRARY

We're going to have an *EVENING* of culture, as well — and listen to these classical records, instead of watching the rubbishy film.

Beethoven

But we haven't seen telly all day! You could at least let us watch the film, Kate.

Beethoven isn't my scene —

Or ours.

You'll grow to like it! A perfect family appreciates good music. Now, let's collect Butch —

Beeth

But later, outside their house —

Woof! Woof!

Hey — steady on, Butch! What's the hurry?

He's after that cat! Oh, no! There's Mr Watson from next door, with his telly! Stop, Butch! *STOP!*

But next second —

Oh, no! Butch has crashed right into him — the telly's smashed!

I'm terribly sorry, Mr Watson. Butch has been cooped up all afternoon at my mother's, and he just went berserk when he saw that cat —

So it seems! We've been decorating the lounge, and I put our telly safely out of the way, at my brother's house. I was just fetching it back, so we could watch the big film tonight — but there's no hope of that now!

Wait, Mr Watson! You can borrow our set — it's the least we can do to make amends.

Thanks for the offer — but we've got piped TV. It needs a special kind of set.

Hey! That gives me an idea —

Mr and Mrs Watson could come round and watch our telly, in our house — couldn't they, Mum?

Of course — that's the answer, Kate.

Er, yes —

That sounds fair enough. And we'll say no more about our damaged set — accidents happen, after all.

Sorry about your evening of classical music, Kate — but we'd better watch the film with the Watsons. It would be rude not to.

Yes, I suppose so. It's a pity this had to happen, though —

Never mind — perfect Mums are perfect neighbours, too, after all.

Mum's day of culture has ended a bit differently to what she planned! My perfect Mum has had to give up on turning us into her perfect family — for one evening, at least!

THE PERFECT MUM

The End

TEA-CUP TALES

China has an ancient tradition of tea-drinking, and from that far-off land came the art of reading the future in a tea-cup. Do YOU want to try it?

First ask your "victim" to drink her tea, leaving only a few dregs at the bottom of the cup. Then she must move the cup three times in a circle, turning it to the LEFT and holding it in her LEFT hand. Finally she must gently turn the cup upside-down in its saucer, and leave it for a few moments to drain.

This is where you start "reading" the tea-leaf shapes left on the sides of the cup — and here is what some of them are said to mean. There will be other tea-leaf pictures, with meanings you can try to interpret by yourself.

If your forecasts don't always work out — well, it's only a bit of fun!

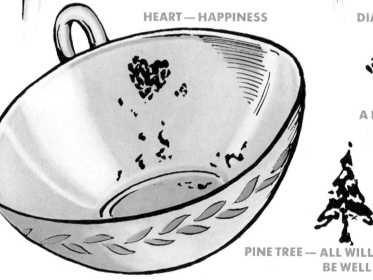

HEART — HAPPINESS

DIAMOND — A PRESENT

PALM TREE — HAPPINESS WITH A BOYFRIEND

TRIANGLE — MYSTERY!

PINE TREE — ALL WILL BE WELL

SPIDER — MONEY IS COMING

CROWN — A WISH WILL BE GRANTED

KEY — GOOD FORTUNE

KEYHOLE — BEWARE OF NOSINESS, BY OTHERS OR YOURSELF!

HAMMER — UNPLEASANT TASKS AWAIT

AXE — YOU WILL OVERCOME DIFFICULTIES

DOG — A TRUE FRIEND

CAT — QUARRELS

SUN — SUCCESS AHEAD

BIRDS — GOOD NEWS

THE LONG AND THE SHORT OF IT!

LINDY LONG, who was *VERY* tall, had made friends with Sally Short, who was very *VERY* small! One weekend, as they practised for the school sports—

Ready, Sally? We'll start off on *YOUR* right foot and *MY* left.

Okay, Lindy. But I don't think we're really suited for the three-legged race.

GO!

Ooh — you're yanking me off my feet!

They landed in a tangled heap!

I told you we'd be no use at that!

Okay — you were right! It's just a pity Carol Smart and Jenny Wilson came along—

Ho! Ho! Were you practising for the comedy race?

We'll give you our one and only ticket for Kevin Wilde's pop concert, if you two clowns win *ANYTHING* at the school sports!

You're on! And if we don't win, you can have the only ticket that *WE'VE* got!

Oh, Lindy — what did you have to agree to that for? I won't win *ANY* event — not with *MY* short legs!

But *I* will! Just leave it to your long-legged pal! I'll do some practising right now — in my garden!

But Lindy's big foot caught in the rope!

43

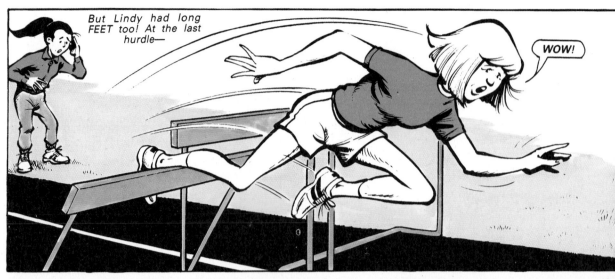

But, suddenly—

My shorts—

They're falling down! Oh, no!

Ha! Ha! That's priceless!

Poor Lindy! She won't win now — and everyone's in kinks!

My new shorts are too big for my skinny waist! I could die of shame!

Lindy muffed every other event, too! And so—

Come on — hand over the ticket!

No — don't! The events might be over for you, Lindy —

— but not for me!

What can YOU enter, Shortie? Is there a midget's race?

WILL COMPETITORS FOR THE OBSTACLE RACE LINE UP, PLEASE?

This is just up my street, Lindy!

Eh?

45

TIME FOR TERROR

AS we motored through the picturesque little village of Burdon Hamlet, I suddenly had the strangest feeling of having been there before.

There was something about the sleepy village that seemed so familiar. I felt a little afraid when Dad stopped the car.

"This looks like a nice place. We'll get something to eat at that little coffee shop," Dad said.

Mum and I got out of the car just behind Dad. Mum couldn't resist taking a few snapshots of the tiny village green and the row of thatched houses nestling beside the pond.

That pond made me shudder. I don't know why, but just looking at it made me feel cold all over.

"I'll just go back to the car and get my jumper," I said, as Mum and Dad made their way into the coffee shop.

I put on my jumper, but didn't go straight back to the coffee shop. Instead, I felt myself being drawn towards the rough wooden seat at the edge of the village pond.

As I gazed into the water, I saw my reflection. At least it *LOOKED* like me, but there seemed to be something different about the girl staring back. She was dressed differently, in very old-fashioned clothes, and she had a look on her face as if she were pleading for help.

Suddenly, I felt a coldness enveloping me and I cried out. I tried to struggle, but my limbs went numb and I lapsed into unconsciousness.

When I awoke, the village had changed. The row of pretty, thatched houses was still there, but where the coffee shop would have been, there was a blacksmith's.

"There she be! Quickly — tie her!" a voice cried.

I was grabbed roughly from behind and a rope was tied around my hands and neck.

I struggled, but my efforts only served to tighten the ropes which bound me.

Several villagers, dressed in mediaeval-style clothes, gathered round and one, a toothless old woman, pointed an accusing finger.

"You be a witch, Jenny Bayliss!" she cried. "And we all knows what happens to witches around these parts!"

There was a loud murmur of agreement from the ever-increasing crowd.

"What are you talking about? My name's Gail Smith," I cried out defiantly. "Let me go!"

"You be Jenny Bayliss all right — and you have the mark of a witch on you. See!"

The old woman grabbed my hands and showed them to the crowd. There was a gasp as she pointed to the index finger of my right hand.

"The mark of the Devil," hissed the old woman. "She pricked her finger on a spinning wheel, while she was making a cloak for the Devil!"

"No! No!" I screamed. "That's not true! I cut my finger on a tin can at home."

I thought back to the day before yesterday when Mum had asked me to open a soup tin, and I'd caught my finger on a jagged edge.

But the ugly crowd was in no mood to listen. One of the men stepped forward.

"She sent a plague of rabbits to devour all my crops!" he exclaimed. "Now my family will starve. We must rid ourselves of this witch here and now!"

The crowd surged forward on a wave of hysteria, and I was lifted bodily upwards and thrown into the pond.

I felt the coldness of the pond enveloping me and I could hear the crowd laughing and jeering as I floundered in the water. Then, all was blackness.

Suddenly, I was aware of being pulled out of the water, and I heard the anxious voice of my mother.

"Gail! Gail! Are you all right? Oh, you silly girl. I've told you not to go near water. You've never been a very good swimmer."

"Oh, Mum," I sobbed, "Take me away from this place, please."

As I sat in the back seat of the car with a travelling rug around me to keep me warm, I watched as we drove past the familiar row of cottages and the luscious grass of the village green.

I *KNEW* I'd been there before!

47

MAKE A G-LOVELY PUPPET!

If you've lost a glove — don't throw the odd one away. Just follow these instructions and turn it into a super duck puppet.

You need:
THE GLOVE
WHITE CARD
CRAYONS
A BOW
GLUE (ask a grown-up which kind to use).

Cut off the three middle fingers of the glove — but make sure you leave the thumb and little finger.

If you don't mind having a hole in this book, cut out the duck's head shown above. Stick it on to stiff card, colour it with crayons when dry, and cut round the outline.

But if you prefer to leave the book intact, then draw or trace the duck's head on to white card. Colour it, and cut it out.

Either way, the next step is to smear glue on the base of the neck. Slip it into the opening where the fingers used to be, and press down firmly.

Cover the join by pinning or gluing on a bow, which may be made from a scrap of ribbon.

Your glove puppet is finished — and you're all set to drive everyone QUACKERS!

48

VALDA AND THE WAY OF THE MESSENGER

A GIRL looked down on the city of Tyros. Her name was Valda—

I feel the call grow stronger. Somewhere in Tyros is one who needs my help.

It is many years since I was here. My task then was beset with dangers — and I sense that I will need all my strength for the perils that lie before me again.

Those young women must be practising for some athletic event.

Suddenly—

That child — he does not heed the car!

Aah — my leg!

That girl saved the child from certain death, but *SHE* is hurt.

Oh, my leg! I'll have to pull out of the race now!

You injured yourself in helping another — but I can heal you!

From the purse at her waist, Valda took a strange crystal—

The sun shines — and the Crystal of Life is ready.

50

The light is blinding, yet she looks straight into it!

The healing powers of the Crystal of Life, passing through my body, will make your leg whole.

Seconds later—

My leg feels fine now — the pain has gone! It's incredible! I was sure it was BROKEN! I'm Sally Young, by the way, and I'm really grateful. Now I still have a chance in the race!

I am Valda, and I am pleased I could help you. I would like to hear more about this race — where is it to be held?

Gosh — you must be the only person in Tryos not to know about the Way of the Messenger. Come and have a coffee, and I'll tell you about it.

The Way of the Messenger? But — that route was closed many, many years ago! And for good reason!

Professor Newman, the archaeologist, traced the route from an ancient manuscript. Then it was decided to hold a women's marathon over the same route — with a prize of £50,000.

It is madness! The race must be stopped!

Don't be silly, Valda! The original runner was a woman, and if SHE managed it, so can we! Besides, the Children's Home where I was brought up needs the prize money. That's why I want to win!

Sally is entering the race for the sake of others, but she is putting her life at risk.

Hi there, Sally! Is your friend also after the big prize?

Valda — this is Eve Skinner, another runner.

I seek no prizes in this life, Eve. Those who run the Way of the Messenger will face many hazards.

I'll be all right — I have a good back-up team. Professor Newman will be giving us all a briefing at the Town Hall tonight, Sally. See you there!

I'm not international class, like Eve — she'll be a tough opponent. But I'll do my best, for the sake of the Children's Home.

That evening—

I know now why I have been called to Tyros. It is to help those who are taking part in this foolhardy enterprise. To do that, I must attend the meeting.

Got your pass ready? No one without a competitor's pass is allowed in.

Valda's eyes fixed the doorman in a piercing stare—

You will let *ME* pass—

Enter, if that is your wish.

It is good. And afterwards, he will not even remember seeing me.

Inside—

The race will take place over three days, with camps for overnight stops. Every runner will be timed for each section, and the times will be added up at the end to find the winner.

So that is Professor Newman. It would be better if he had never uncovered the Way of the Messenger!

There will be a number of hazards, and competitors will need to look for the clues that show the original way.

He knows not of the *GREATEST* peril!

52

I lost twenty minutes today. I'll need help to make up time tomorrow.

Eve is plotting trouble with the leader of her back-up team. I will be especially watchful tomorrow.

Next day—

Eve has made a really fast start.

Let her go— she'll soon tire herself out.

Suddenly, there was a rumble, like thunder—

Look out—

We could have been killed! And now our path is blocked!

I am sure that this was Eve's doing!

Then the runners witnessed an amazing feat of strength—

Look at that! She's pushing all those rocks aside!

Valda has incredible strength! But not just that — there's something strange, weird, about her!

55

There was a small explosion, before the rumble of the falling rocks — and there are burn marks here! Eve's back-up team did their evil work well!

That's right! She ran round the barbarian horde who wanted to kill the Crown Prince, and warned him. But — how did you know that?

History is not only recorded in ancient documents, Professor. It also lives on in people's hearts.

Rubbish! You know nothing about it! I'm going the easy way.

Later, at a checkpoint—

I hear you came to the rescue, back at the pass. Why are you running with us, Valda? Are you competing?

Not all who run the Way of the Messenger are competitors, Professor. The original messenger ran to prevent an uprising — many lives were saved because of her.

That's the way we must take. It looks easier.

No! You are wrong! That way leads to danger — take the other way!

Valda has already been a guardian angel to us all. I'll take her advice.

She could be right — that marker must have been carved in the stone, ages ago.

You advised us to go this way, Valda. Aren't you coming with us?

These foolish ones need my help, Sally. I will see you later.

AAAH!

It is as I feared. This way is still crumbling — it is perilous indeed!

So we come to the last day of the race, Sally. I must warn you, the greatest dangers are still ahead.

It's almost as though you know the route, Valda. I wish *I* did! Eve Skinner has caught up with me on times — I'll have a hard job to win.

May I suggest that you change the route, and use the new road down the mountain, Professor?

That's out of the question! The sponsors insist on following the original Way.

Then I beg you to hold back the runners from the Pass of Khomas, until I give the signal.

How does she know the ancient name? There's something very odd about this girl.

I — I'll see how things go, Valda. I can't promise anything at the moment.

Valda sped off ahead of the others—

Valda's got a good lead on us. She makes out she's not competing, but I'd like to know what her game is.

Soon—

I suggest you all stay put until this fog clears. It will be safer!

Valda's got her way — she wanted them held back!

I'M not staying here! I'm going to follow Valda.

There is no sunlight, but the Crystal gives me enough power to find my way in this evil gloom.

This is where the Dark One waits for his prey, like a spider in a giant web.

59

AAAH!

Your greed for power has destroyed you!

Nothing remains of the Dark One, save this cloak. Even his evil fog melts away.

Look — it's the signal from Valda. You can go forward now.

I want a long talk with that girl, when the race is over. She knows things that no living soul has learned — except me!

Eve is missing. And I hear a faint cry in the distance!

Moira burst into the kitchen and flung down her school case.

"We're going to have a sponsored swim to raise funds for the hospital, Mum — to buy a kidney machine. Isn't it great? Miss Dawson wants all of us who can swim to enter. It's next Friday. I can't *wait* for it! Anne says —"

"Pick up that case from the floor," Moira's mother said firmly, "and take that damp swim-suit and towel off my clean ironing."

Moira grumbled a bit at being stopped at full spate, but she was like a rubber ball and soon was as bouncy as ever.

"Now tell me all about it," said her mother.

"We are going to ask our families and friends to sponsor us. If you sponsored me at five pence a length, and I swam fifteen lengths straight off, that would be seventy-five pence you would give me for the fund, and if Dad promised me ten pence a length, that would be another one pound fifty pence, and then if Simon—"

"Steady on," Mum said, laughing. "This family isn't made of money! Still, we'll do our best, no doubt, and when Dad comes home perhaps he'll join in too."

Moira's father was away on a business trip and would not be back until after the swim.

For the next few days, Moira talked about the contest until the family became tired of hearing of it.

"I'll probably do the greatest number of lengths from the first formers, because I'm the best swimmer there," she announced at breakfast when the great day arrived. "Anne thinks she can beat me, but she won't! She begins to fade after twelve lengths, when I'm still quite fresh."

"Don't brag," said her elder brother, Simon. "You might swallow some water and end up last, and it would serve you right for showing off in that nauseating fashion."

"You're an old meanie," Moira said indignantly. "I'm not showing off, I'm just trying to help the hospital. I think you're cross because *your* school didn't think of a sponsored swim first."

"Don't argue, you two," Mum said.

"But really, Mum — with all the fuss she's making, you'd think she was preparing to swim the Channel!"

In spite of the arguing, Simon agreed to sponsor at one penny a length, and their eight-year-old brother John at a halfpenny. Mum stuck at three pence.

"Now go off to school, the three of you, and give me a little peace. I hope you do well, Moira."

At half past four, Moira came in full of bounce and glee.

"I swam twenty-one lengths, better than lots of the second and third formers who didn't come anywhere near that! Anne only did fifteen lengths. I knew I could beat her!"

"I'm glad you did well, dear, but fifteen is

A SPELL of SUCCESS

very good for Anne. That's the best she has ever done, isn't it?"

"Yes. But I knew she wouldn't beat me."

"Of all the boasters!" Simon had come in unnoticed. "Why have I been afflicted with such a sister?"

"You can say what you like, but Dad will be pleased with me, I know. That's sixty-three pence you owe me, Mum."

Their father came back the next day, just in time for Saturday tea, a time all the family enjoyed. Moira rushed up to him the moment he appeared, and began to tell him how well she had done in the swim, and how many people she had beaten.

"So you'll sponsor me, won't you, Dad? How much will you give?"

"Now then, pipe down! I've only just come in the door. I want to hear Mum's news, and have a good look at you all. John, you've grown." John giggled. He was rather small for his age, but Dad said this every time he went away, even for a week.

"And we want to hear *your* news," Mum said. "How did things go?"

Moira sulked for a minute or so, and murmured something about nobody ever wanting to hear about her, but quite soon she was her own bouncy self again.

Their father had brought back small presents for everybody; foreign stamps, some nature books, and scent for Mum. Then amid the joyful chatter of Saturday tea, Moira's insistent voice was heard: "You'll give me ten pence a length, won't you, Dad?"

"No — fifty pence the lot, and think yourself lucky! I've had a lot of expenses lately."

"Daddy, I told all the girls you'd give me quite a lot if I did well. It *is* mean!"

Then John, who never talked much, came out with what was for him, quite a speech.

"I thought when people got sponsored, they did it for the charity, not to show how clever they were. When Tim Goodson got back from his sponsored walk and I asked him how many miles he had done, he just laughed and said he couldn't remember — only that his feet were killing him, but it was all in a good cause. The others said he was marvellous, but he didn't show off — like *you* Moira."

"That's not fair," Moira protested. "Is it, Dad?"

"We-ll, there's something in what John says. You earned money the easy way, and you are certainly crowing a lot over it. Here's an offer." Dad pulled an old spelling book out of the bookcase. "I know you kids think I'm a bit of a square, but I happen to think spelling is important! There are forty words a page, and fifty pages in this book. I'll give you five pence for the hospital for each page, when you can spell it without a mistake."

Spelling! Oh! Moira looked dismayed. She was hopeless at spelling.

"That sounds awfully dull!" she exclaimed. "There's not much fun in learning words."

"And not much fun, if you are ill, to be told that there's no kidney machine available, to help you," Simon put in.

Moira felt rather ashamed. She certainly had taken on the swim because it gave her the chance to shine. It was not very sporting to turn down *this* offer.

"Right, Daddy. Thank you, I'll start today."

The first seven pages were quite easy, and Moira tossed the words off gaily. But, oh dear — soon she found it tough going. "This page of words with silent letters, like 'k-n-o-m-e' —"

"Whatever's that?" enquired Mum.

"Oh, bother — it's 'g-n-o-m-e'. And page forty-five is full of words like chrysanthemum, and sepulchre, and rhinoceros. I daren't look at page fifty, I'd probably pass out."

Moira plodded on, with a few setbacks, for the rules were strictly kept and if she mis-spelt a word it meant going over the page again. But every time she dropped a five pence coin into her collecting box, she felt a nice warm feeling.

At last the end was in sight. Page forty-five took some hard work to master, and the whole family cheered when Moira got through it successfully. She really had earned *that* five pence!

To her surprise, she found she was enjoying it.

"Miss Hodges can't understand what's happened to my spelling," she told the family. "Only one mistake in my last essay, and it was seventeen a month ago!"

At last she was at page fifty. That really was difficult! And sometimes she thought she would never get through it. But Dad heard her one Saturday evening, ending up with a flourish with 'rhododendron'. He was delighted, and said: "Well done, Moira!"

"How will you give in the money?" Simon enquired.

It would be nice to hand over her two pounds fifty pence to the Matron, and get her grateful thanks, and those of any doctors who happened to be around. But no — Moira sighed as she decided that was not the way, and on a drizzly Monday morning she set off for school, clutching the two pounds fifty Dad had given her, saying that he was proud of her.

She splashed her way up the hospital steps and into the vestibule. There was a collecting box fixed to the wall, marked FOR THE KIDNEY MACHINE. Moira slipped her money into it, and hurried off to school. The sun had come out, and it had stopped raining.

* * *

A week later Moira bounded into the kitchen after school.

"Mum, what do you think? We're going to have—"

"*Mind* those cakes just out of the oven — Yes, dear?"

"There's going to be a General Knowledge and Spelling Quiz, our school against the boys of St John's — one pupil from each form. The parents are invited, and there will be a collection for "The Save The Children Fund". It will be held in our school hall. And guess who has been chosen to spell for our first form?"

"Moira Watson?"

"*Yes!*" Moira replied, her face one big beam.

What's Cooking?

Some puzzles and a simple recipe to keep you busy. The puzzle answers are given at the bottom of the page.

IN A JAM!

Hidden in each of the following sentences is a fruit that makes a delicious jam or jelly. Can you find them?

1. The customer had ample money to spend.

2. He gave the ape a chair to sit on.

3. Susan or Angela will be the winner.

4. "May I have that cap, please?" asked the boy.

5. The Adams only have one daughter.

POT LUCK

Susie's in hot water — everything's boiling over! Unscramble the letters to find what's in each pot.

COOK UP A SNOWMAN'S FACE

This winter recipe will bring a smile to the frostiest face. Serve it with sausages or burgers, for a tasty supper.

INGREDIENTS:—
1 large packet of instant potato for the face.
1 hard-boiled egg for eyes.
1 small tinned carrot for nose.
Some tomato for lips and eyebrows.

METHOD:—
In a bowl, make up the instant potato as directed on packet. Turn out on to a board or flat dish and shape into a round face. Add the nose, eyes, lips and eyebrows. Do this quickly or potato will get cold.

SUGAR AND SPICE

In this mixture is an ODD-ONE-OUT — neither sugar nor spice, but a herb! But which is it? (The first letters of each answer, put in the spice jars, will CRYSTALLIZE this!)

1. Green and candied usually. Sticky! Similar to rhubarb sticks in size, though sold in mini-size in the shops. (8 letters) _____

2. When whole, looks like an oval nut. Often grated on to milk puddings. 1st part of word appears already in this clue. 2nd part of word is a gem backwards! (6 letters) _____

3. Root of a plant which is scaled and dried. Can be crystallized, too. Hot, spicy taste. Clue — A chum with auburn hair could be called this! (6 letters) _____

4. Vanilla, almond, lemon, peppermint — all these flavourings are also called an ------- (7 letters) _____

5. Made from cane or sugar-beet. This lump-type is served with tea or coffee. Clue to 1st part — A ---- of bread. Clue to 2nd part — Appears already in this question! (4 and 5 letters) _____

6. Also made from either cane or beet. VERY fine! Used in cake decoration. (5 and 5 letters) _____

7. A dried, unopened flower bud. Looks like a small nail head. You COULD squeeze one on to an aching tooth to take away toothache. (5 letters) _____

8. This fruit of a plant is used as a flavouring AND colouring in confectionery, cordials, etc. (7 letters) _____

FOOD FOR THOUGHT

Walter the waiter is in a pickle — he can't remember who ordered what! Can you help him to match up the dish to the diner?

PAELLA   **CURRY**   **RAW FISH**   **SNAILS**

1   2   3   4

ANSWERS

FOOD FOR THOUGHT: PAELLA — 4. CURRY — 1. RAW FISH — 2. SNAILS — 3.
ODD-ONE-OUT: ANGELICA.
7. CLOVE, 8. ANISEED.
SUGAR AND SPICE: 1. ANGELICA, 2. NUTMEG, 3. GINGER, 4. ESSENCE, 5. LOAF-SUGAR, 6. ICING-SUGAR.
POT LUCK: Clockwise from top left, RICE, CURRY, SOUP, STEW.
IN A JAM: 1. Lemon, 2. Peach, 3. Orange, 4. Apple, 5. Damson.

A Little Bit Of Sunshine

MY Gran Bruce, who brought me up, was the kindest person I ever knew. She was always giving—

Buy young Colin new shoes with this money, dear.

Your purse is empty, Gran — that was the last of your pension you gave away.

I know, Avril — but there's always next week's. Anyway, Mrs Watson has a struggle bringing up two children, with her husband dead.

Another night—

I'm sure I heard Gran slipping out. Where could she be going, at two o'clock in the morning?

I found her in the flat upstairs.

You get some sleep, Wilma, I'll sit up with David.

Thanks, Gran Bruce — I'm done in.

Gran's always looking after our neighbours' sick kids, day and night. She's got a heart of gold.

Gran even gave her food away.

Where's *YOUR* piece of steak, Gran?

Oh, old Mr Roberts downstairs is off his food. I thought a bit of steak might tempt him—

The way I see it is — we only pass through this world once. So why not leave a bit of sunshine behind?

One day, when Gran and I were out shopping—

COCKER SPANIEL PUPS FOR SALE

Aren't these pups in the pet shop magic? I've always wanted a spaniel, Gran.

Then you'll have one for your birthday next week, Avril. You're old enough to take proper care of a pet now.

I was over the moon. But on the way home—

Oh, look at that poor dog, raking in the bin — he must be starving!

Bring him up and we'll give him something to eat. He must be a stray.

A stray who's landed lucky. Gran will spoil him rotten!

66

She's given him her share of the stew — that's just typical of Gran!

Later—

I haven't the heart to turn him out again, Avril. I know he's a mongrel, and not as cute as the pups in the pet shop — but what about keeping him instead? You can have something else for your birthday—

All right, Gran. I like him, too.

But the dog was unclaimed. So he became mine, and I called him Dillon — because I thought it was a nice name for a dog.

Oh, I'm so glad. I'll make some phone calls first — to check that he doesn't belong to anyone.

He's put on pounds, with Gran's feeding. I really love him! Now I've got a super dog AND a super Gran!

But, several weeks later—

There's an ambulance parked outside our block of flats — I wonder who's ill?

My Gran? Oh, no — what's happened to her?

She was taking in someone's washing, when she collapsed. Don't worry, lass — she's going to be fine.

67

And sure enough—

Will he still be here in the morning, when I wake up?

Yes, love. That was a brainwave, Avril.

Time passed, and one day—

I've been wanting to enter Dillon for a pet show — so now's my chance. There's a class mentioned here that he's BOUND to win!

But, back at the Home—

Please can I take Dillon to the pet show on Saturday, Avril?

Er — all right, Terry.

And so—

THE DOG with the WAGGIEST TAIL

Terry was so desperate to do it — I couldn't say no. Besides Matron says I'll have a chance to be fostered soon — so I'll have Dillon all to myself then.

The following week—

I've been asked to tea by this couple, Mr and Mrs Donald. I wouldn't mind staying with them for keeps — they're both so nice.

There's even a great big garden for Dillon to romp about in!

To my delight, the Donalds wanted me — and soon, it was all settled. But, when Matron told the children that Dillon and I would be leaving—

Can't Dillon stay? We love him so much, Matron!

I know, Jane — but he's Avril's dog.

They're all shattered because Dillon's going. I knew they were fond of him, but I didn't realise just how much.

Then I overheard Matron talking on the phone—

It was a mistake letting Avril keep her dog here. The news of Dillon going has upset the children badly—

And suddenly, I knew exactly what I had to do!

I just came to say that I don't think the Donalds are too keen on dogs, Matron. So if it's all right — can Dillon stay here?

Well, if you're sure, dear. The other children will certainly be happy to keep him.

I was sure, all right — though parting with Dillon cost me more heartache than they ever knew.

Bye, Dillon — I'll miss you so much, but I know I'm doing the right thing.

After all, I had a whole new life to look forward to. And, besides—

I'm only doing what Gran would have done — "leaving a little bit of sunshine behind."

THE END

I Won't Spoil Her Wedding!

YOUNG Angie Telford had a beautiful china doll, which had been her sister's, her Mum's — and her Gran's before that!

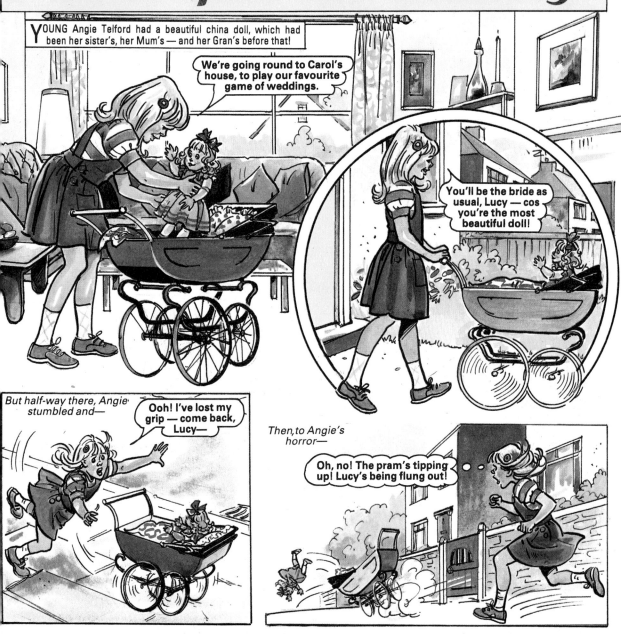

We're going round to Carol's house, to play our favourite game of weddings.

You'll be the bride as usual, Lucy — cos you're the most beautiful doll!

But half-way there, Angie stumbled and—

Ooh! I've lost my grip — come back, Lucy—

Then, to Angie's horror—

Oh, no! The pram's tipping up! Lucy's being flung out!

Oh, Lucy — your poor face! It — it's all smashed!

Broken-hearted, Angie wheeled Lucy home again.

Lucy's ugly now, Mum! She — she'll never be a bride in my games again—

Hush, Angie — I know who can help.

And, later in a quiet back street—

TOBIAS — TOYS MENDED

TOYS MENDED

Tobias the toy-mender used to mend my broken toys when I was your age — he can work magic. I'm sure he'll be able to mend Lucy.

Oh, Mum — I hope he can!

Leave Lucy with me, Angie. Old Tobias will make her as good as new!

Oh, thank you — thank you very much!

How's that, then?

Her face is just perfect again — there's not even a tiny crack showing. Thank you, Mr Tobias — you *CAN* work magic!

In the years that followed, old Tobias mended many toys for Angie — and listened to her problems, too! When Angie was twelve—

That's your musical box fixed. I reckon you won't be needing my services much from now on. You're growing past the toy stage!

But pop in, if ever I can help you in *ANY* way, Angie.

Thanks, Tobias! I'll remember that!

Two years passed—

Angie — Colin and I are engaged! We want you to be our bridesmaid!

Wow, what a super ring, Sis! Congrats to both of you—

72

— and I'd *LOVE* to be your bridesmaid! It's what I've always dreamed of, Jill!

It will be a fairy tale wedding, cos Jill's so beautiful and Colin's handsome — and I'm quite pretty, too! Oh, I can't wait!

Three months before the wedding—

I'm driving down to Great-Aunt Emily's house in the country, to collect a wedding present she has for us. Like to come, Angie? Colin's working today.

I'd love to, Jill!

But, as Jill drove out of town—

Jill — look out!

Jill swerved to avoid the dog, but crashed into a lamp-post!

Ooh!

Aaagh!

I've phoned for help—

My face! My face! It's covered in blood!

Calm down, Angie. The ambulance is on its way.

Shortly after—

We'll soon whisk you to hospital, girls.

My — my young sister got the worst of it! Her face is terribly cut!

Later, in hospital—

They're keeping you in for a couple of days for observation, pet. You're coming along fine—

But my face, Mum! Will — will IT be fine?

And, a few days later—

Oh, NO! I've got horrible ugly scars on both my cheeks!

Cheer up, love! Plastic surgery works wonders. You'll see—

But, on the day when Angie left hospital—

I'm afraid Angie will have to wait six months for plastic surgery. It's the soonest it can be done.

SIX months! But — but Jill's wedding is in THREE!

75

You look lovely in it, Angie!

Yes, really pretty.

Mum and Jill left Angie alone. But, minutes later—

They ARE ugly — aren't they, Jill?

Not half, Mum!

Oh!

Huh! I might be, if it wasn't for my scars. But somehow even THEY don't look too ugly right now, either. Maybe I will be a bridesmaid after all!

You're talking about my scars — you were only PRETENDING that you thought I looked nice! Find yourself another bridesmaid, Jill Telford — I —I'm taking this off!

Oh, Angie! We were talking about the vases Jill got for a wedding present — not you!

And I want YOU as my bridesmaid — nobody else!

NO! No — I couldn't face it!

Soon after—

How's that? You can hardly see the scars now!

Oh, yes you can! They still show through!

The following night—

Meet Karen, Angie — she's a chum of mine, and a beautician. She's going to see if she can disguise your scars with make-up, for the wedding.

It's impossible!

We'll see — shall we?

Thanks for trying, Karen — but I look like a clown in all this make-up!

I won't be your bridesmaid — I won't spoil your wedding, Jill! Why can't you accept it?

All right, love. I suppose I have to.

Now I know how *YOU* must have felt, Lucy — with your smashed-up face. But old Tobias mended yours, good as new. If only he could do the same for mine!

That night—

Still, Tobias told me to visit him, if ever I needed help! And I do — even if it's only someone to tell my troubles to! Maybe I'll call on him tomorrow.

So, next day—

I'm off to visit a friend, Mum.

All right, love. We're up to our necks here, with the wedding-guest list!

I brought you with me, Lucy, cos Tobias is *YOUR* old friend, too! Oh, it will be good to see him again.

But, in the quiet back street—

His shop's all closed up! And — and there's a funeral procession leaving his little house next door! Oh, no — it can't be—

Poor old Tobias.

That illness finished him.

It IS his funeral! Tobias is dead!

I'll never have that chat with him now — or show him my scarred, ugly face! I've come too late!

CEMETERY

At the cemetery, Angie spoke words of farewell —

Goodbye, Tobias. Thank you for mending Lucy's face.

He fixed my toy soldier, too!

Oh! Did he?

He did! And I'VE come to thank him, too!

78

I'm sure EVERYONE does! I'm ugly — too ugly to be bridesmaid at my sister's wedding.

CEMETER

I — I came to see him today — to show him MY face! I knew he couldn't patch IT up, but he would have been so kind, to tell all my troubles to.

Yes, I noticed your scars.

Maybe I can help—

Later, back home—

Angie — you're soaked!

I visited old Tobias — but ended up at his funeral! He's dead, Mum!

But, that evening—

Wow! He's come!

Are you Mr Telford? I'm Ralph Hunt — and I'd like to help Angie.

Please come in, Mr Hunt — and explain!

Poor love! I'll towel your hair!

Here's a hot drink!

I won't tell them about the man with the toy soldier — or that he said he could help, and asked for our address. What could HE do?

79

Old Tobias mended *MY* toys, too — when I was a little lad. I used to watch, fascinated, as he made dolls' smashed faces pretty again. *HE* inspired me to be what I am today—

— a plastic surgeon, who can mend *REAL* faces! I'd be happy to make *YOUR* face as good as new, Angie! It would be my way of saying "thanks" to Tobias.

Oh — that would be marvellous, Mr Hunt!

A few days later, Angie entered Mr Hunt's private clinic for plastic surgery.

That's the operation over, Angie. But the bandages have to stay on for two weeks.

Oh, Mum — I can't wait for them to come off!

And, when they did—

How's that then, Angie?

My face is normal again — there's not even a tiny scar to be seen! Oh, thank you — thank you! Now I can be Jill's bridesmaid after all!

Mr Hunt was a special guest at the most beautiful wedding, ever! And, as pretty bridesmaid Angie followed her sister down the aisle—

My ugly scars have gone forever! Tobias has gone, too — but somehow I feel that he's right here, in church, smiling at my face which *HE* helped to mend — through Mr Hunt!

THE END

LAURA AND THE Little People

That's odd. The turkey's been in the oven for ages — but all I can smell is fried onions!

BACK in the summer, Laura Dobson had discovered a family of fairies living at the bottom of her garden. But they were tough, scruffy fairies — banished from Fairyland until they behaved like proper GOOD fairies! Their sloppy spells got Laura into a lot of difficulties, but eventually she persuaded the fairy authorities to take them back.

It was Christmas morning and Laura was looking forward to her dinner.

It's terribly strong — I wonder where it could be coming from? What's that?

This is a bit of all right, innit?

It's Ma and Pa Fairy! Don't tell me you've been thrown out of Fairyland AGAIN!

Course we ain't. We've come to spend Christmas with you. Ma's fry-ups are great, but she's not so good with turkey.

You might have warned me. I thought I'd seen the last of your family. And that reminds me — where are the children?

You don't 'alf ask some daft questions. It's our Bernadette's turn to go on top of the Christmas tree, innit?

Hiya, Laura! Not many people have REAL fairies on their trees, y'know.

Hello, Kevin. I suppose you're right.

And I don't suppose many Christmas tree fairies eat all the sweets off the branches either. Mum can't see you — nobody can, unless they BELIEVE in fairies — so guess who'll get the blame?

I'm off with my brother Ian to take a Christmas card to one of our neighbours. No more frying onions while I'm gone!

Munch! No fear — munch! Munch! We're looking forward to our dinner. We don't want to spoil it by eating too much breakfast. Munch!

Miss Hill was delighted to see Laura and Ian.

What a lovely card! I'll put it on the mantelpiece, with the one my nephew sent me.

Poor Miss Hill — fancy only having two Christmas cards.

But I thought your nephew always came to stay with you at this time of year.

He always used to, but earlier this year he emigrated to Australia. He could hardly come all the way back, just to see me.

No, I suppose not.

83

LOVE thy NEIGHBOUR

CAROL BROWN and Brian Grey lived next door to each other in Harmony Avenue. They were the best of friends — but their two families couldn't stand each other, despite Brian and Carol's efforts to bring them together.

Carol's father was very keen on his hobby.

I've got a model next door, Carol —

Oh, dear! Sorry, Dad — I didn't realise, and I let Rex in!

Oh, no! I spent most of last night working on this wing! Let go, you stupid animal!

Dad thinks the world of his model aircraft — I just wish he'd told me there was one in here.

Is it okay?

Well, it's a bit chewed — but it's nothing I can't fix.

Thank goodness for that. I really am sorry, Dad.

I'm sorry I blamed you for letting Rex in — it was my own fault for not warning you. I can't expect you or your sister Sandra to take an interest in my hobby, and James is too young to be any help.

That's okay, Dad. I understand.

And it's given me an idea — I think it's time BRIAN took up model-making.

Brian was in his back garden, with his parents.

I suppose model-making would make a change from golf, golf and more golf. That's all MY Mum and Dad seem to think about.

I know — I've seen them playing, when I've been to the model aero club with Dad. It's right next to the golf course.

87

It didn't take long to get to the golf course.

Here we are — this is the clubhouse. What do you think of it?

It's very smart — and much bigger than I thought!

There's even a proper ballroom. And that gives me an idea — do you think your parents would like to come to one of our Social Evenings with us?

DINNER DANCE NEXT WEEK

I'm sure they would.

Then Mum and Dad will have to invite the Greys back, and our family feud will be over!

Mr Grey introduced Carol to everyone.

This is Major Jones, our Club Captain. He's playing a match, so we'll let him and his opponent go first.

Pleased to meet you, Major.

Right — it's my turn to tee off. If I can concentrate, with all the noise from that blasted model aircraft!

Oh-oh! That particular plane looks very familiar. I'll keep my fingers crossed, and hope the Greys don't recognise it as Dad's!

They've switched the engine off, thank goodness. Now at least I can hear myself think again.

The engine's cut, all right — but only because the plane's going to crash. And it's heading right for us!

LOOK OUT!

Mr Grey stepped back — on to the model, which had rolled to a halt right behind him!

The End

MAKING FACES *with MANDY*

DRAWING faces isn't difficult if you follow a few simple rules:
    Start off with an egg shape. Now mark lightly, with pencil, where you want to put the eyes, nose and mouth. The eyes will come about halfway down the oval, the bottom of the nose about two-thirds of the way down. The mouth line will be not quite halfway between the nose line and the bottom of the oval.

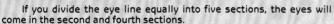

If you divide the eye line equally into five sections, the eyes will come in the second and fourth sections.
    Now draw in almond shapes for eyes. Thicken the top line for eyelashes, thinning it slightly towards the centre.
    Draw in the eyeball and pupil.
    Draw a curve above the eye for the eyelid. Mark in curves above the eyes for eyebrows. Eyebrows are longer than the eye itself and become heavier towards the centre.

Noses look more realistic if you DON'T draw in all the lines. Just mark in the bottom curves and use light, curved lines at the top.

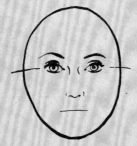

The length of the mouth line can be measured by putting faint guidelines — directly under each eyeball centre — across the mouth line already marked in. Fill in the upper lip with a "bow" shape, and suggest the lower lip with just a small curve underneath.

Ears can be marked in from the top of the eye to the base of the nose. Just suggest them with light, curved lines.

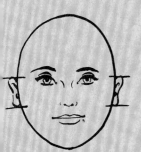

Now you can have fun with the hair! And finally, rub out all the guidelines.

To draw a particular person, follow the above directions, but look very closely at your subject. Small variations from the basic shape give faces their individuality. Some people will have wider or thinner faces, some will have larger or smaller features. It takes practice to notice the differences, and to put them down on paper.

Older faces have lost their youthful elasticity, so that the face falls into lines and folds. Lines around the eyes, mouth and forehead will be pronounced, the chin line less definite, giving the impression of a "double chin". Faces are usually thinner than young people's.

Babies and small children are just the opposite. The face is plump and rounded, the skin clear and smooth. Features are small, relative to the face size, and the eyebrows are sparse. The hair is usually very fine.

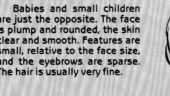

The Sing-a-Gram Girl

SENGA WINSLOW lived with her mean aunt, Kate Crabbe, who owned a newsagent's shop in Birtonham. But Senga was also the town's Sing-a-Gram Girl — she had a fine singing voice, and she could make up a song for any occasion.

BATLEY'S holiday camp SILVERSEA

Here's your order, Mrs Cleese. One pound fifteen, if you please.

I hear you're doing a Sing-a-Gram at the opening of Batley's Holiday Camp, at Silversea. We'll be there to hear you, Senga.

Who are you going with, Mrs Cleese? And I don't know about any Sing-a-Gram!

Aunt Kate butted in —

Oh, didn't I tell you, Senga? Mrs Cleese and I have been invited to stay for the opening week — by Mr Batley himself. You'll look after the shop — it's your mid-term week's holiday. You can close early on Saturday afternoon, so that you can get to the camp in time for your Sing-a-Gram.

Big deal! Aunt Kate's all heart — I don't think!

Later, Senga met her pals, Doris Green and Pat Wilson.

Imagine! My crafty old aunt has wangled a week at a holiday camp, as payment for a Sing-a-Gram sung by ME! I have to go to Batley's camp on Saturday.

We'll come with you, Senga. My Dad will drive us down in the van.

On Saturday forenoon —

Remember, Senga — you'll close the shop at four-thirty, and get the five o'clock bus to Silversea. Then, after your Sing-a-Gram, you can get the last bus back — so you can open the shop on Sunday.

Yes, I've got it, Aunt Kate — have a good holiday!

CRABBE Newsagent & Tobacconist

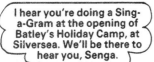

Then, at two o'clock —

Off you go, Senga. I'll look after the shop till closing time.

Thanks, Mrs Green. But what's happened to the van?

Our lad Joe is playing in a group. This is their van now, and all their gear is in it.

Later —

Here we are, then — Batley's!

Senga found Bert Batley at reception, but —

Ah, the Sing-a-Gram Girl! It sounded a good idea when I booked you — but now we're short of waitresses, got no band — and three of my Redcoats have walked out!

The three girls were all junior members of the Birtonham People's Theatre.

Lend us some uniforms, and leave the rest to me, Mr Batley. Senga's Sing-a-Grams aim to please. Come on, Doris — lend a hand, Pat —

Okay, gang. Now we're Redcoats — so give it bags of pep and zip. I've done a welcome song — to the tune of "I Do Like To Be Beside The Seaside" —

94

Later, in the concert hall —

TONIGHT THE REDCOAT REVELS

Thanks for agreeing to help out when I phoned you, Joe — everything okay?

I think so, Senga — fingers crossed!

The show started with Senga's Sing-a-Gram — to the campers, from Bert Batley.

Hi-de-hi and hey-di-hey, This is Batley's opening day. Hi-de-hi and ho-di-ho Settle back, enjoy the show.

SING-A-GRAM

Then Doris and Pat joined in —

Happy days are here again, All the folks at Batley's cheer again, To the concert hall they steer again, Happy days are here again!

Fortunately the camp comic had arrived —

Funny thing happened to me on the way to Silversea today — I heard a new joke!

Later, Senga sang songs from some musical shows —

Somewhere over the rainbow, Skies are blue —

Later, the Zooms provided music for dancing.

The Redcoats have *GOT* to join in the fun! Phew!

Senga, with the camp comic and the girls, kept the show going all night. At last —

Goodnight, campers. See you all tomorrow. Each one happy — not a sign of sorrow —

You kids are magic! Stay for the week, till I get a full staff organised. I'll pay you well —

Sorry, Mr Batley. I'd be glad of a bed tonight — but I have to get back to open my aunt's shop tomorrow.

Senga's tight-fisted Aunt Kate couldn't let a full week's trading go by — she went home.

But Bert Batley was determined that the girls should stay. Next morning —

You're not on, Miss Crabbe. You can't have a girl of fourteen workin' in a shop all week — it's illegal. Someone might tip off the cops — someone like me! If you want your shop open, then go home and open it yourself!

Well!

That's telling Senga

Funny! It never dawned on Aunt Kate that it's just as illegal for me to work in a holiday camp!

This isn't work — it's paid fun! And it's all thanks to the Sing-a-Gram Girl!

THE END

The Foundling

I LOVED that little fellow from the moment I first saw him, and when I think of the joy he brought into our lives — well, let me start at the beginning.

Working at a Children's Home, I am always surrounded by children of all ages — from tiny tots to those about to set off for work for the very first time and make their own way in life.

It happened like this, how we came to have Jimmy, without knowing anything about him.

I had been to the village Post Office, and I came back to the Home via a short cut, through the copse. People had been dumping all sorts of rubbish there, garden refuse mostly, sometimes a battered old armchair or an old mattress. It was an eyesore as well as a nuisance.

However, on this particular morning, my eyes seemed drawn to a pile of assorted jumble near the path. It had been dumped quite recently, judging by the dryness of the newspapers and magazines. Then, to my surprise, I saw a tiny face just visible beneath a discarded old cardigan! There was a little snub nose, a rosebud mouth, and two appealing brown eyes were looking at me.

Quickly, but gently, I lifted the cardigan and gathered up a limp little body. There was no sound or movement, his little limbs had no strength. I carried him back with me to the Home and did what I could for him. After a while, I realised he was not entirely lifeless.

Of course, I had to report my finding him, for it surprised me how anyone could just abandon a helpless little figure like Jimmy, which I had decided to name him.

The authorities had no objection to my keeping him, it was clearly a case of his being unwanted. Fortunately, he had been found by a most suitable person, a Children's Home worker!

Poor Jimmy, he had simply no control over his movements, so stiff and jerky was he. But his little face was so cheerful, the children all loved him, and he got more attention than most!

I didn't know what we did before Jimmy came to stay, there was laughter and fun with him every day. But even Jimmy needed to rest sometimes, usually in my room, where it was quieter.

Gradually Jimmy's limbs began to move more smoothly, he could do some things the children could — and others which they couldn't. But though Jimmy couldn't talk, he could make himself understood.

He even had invitations to other Children's Homes, to parties, and no Christmas was complete without Jimmy and his amusing little ways. He became a great favourite with all ages.

If children were unwell, we would take Jimmy to see them. If they were very sick, he would sit on the bed quietly. But if they were in need of cheering up, he could soon make them smile, by dancing round the room, and showing them his little antics.

There was a time one of the boys had a plaster-cast on a broken leg. Jimmy insisted we put *HIS* leg in plaster too. The idea being, if the leg was stiff when the plaster was removed, Jimmy could show the lad how to get it moving again. Oh, Jimmy helped us in so many ways.

Then one day, after many happy years of fun with Jimmy, I became very ill. I just lay in bed unable to move. It affected Jimmy more than most — others tried to help him, but it was clear he missed and needed me. I suppose he rather depended on me. I was flattered, but felt so sorry for him.

I was a long time getting better, and then I had to exercise my wasted limbs. How it reminded me of the state Jimmy was in when I found him!

They brought Jimmy to me for encouragement, and I was overjoyed to see him! In no time at all, he had me walking up and down the room with him, and moving my weakened arms and fingers, until I felt my strength coming back. Without Jimmy's help, I would have been ages recovering.

From then on, life continued as before, and Jimmy made more and more friends, as new children came to stay in the Home.

The girls liked to knit little hats and scarves for him, and the boys made things. There was a small chair for him to sit on, a swing, and a truck they could pull along with him in it. So you can imagine he was very pampered! But I must tell you — unlike his little playmates, our Jimmy would never grow up.

Then, quite unexpectedly one day, Jimmy collapsed! His little legs wouldn't do what he wanted them to do, one arm lay absolutely limp and useless alongside him. Needless to say, the children were all heart-broken.

I knew what to do. A bit of string here, a knot there, and a twiddle about, soon had Jimmy up and about again, and back to his usual perky self — to the delight of the children.

After all these years, his worn out strings had given way, and he needed new ones.

No one *EVER* had a puppet quite like Jimmy!

Lucy's Loving Cake

LUCY DAVIS made a cake from bewitched flour — and found that anyone who ate a slice became especially "loving"!

Auntie Grace has just phoned. Uncle Dan's ill, and she wants you to go over and give them a hand this weekend. Will you go?

Oh, Mum! I like the farm, but I can't stand my cousin Beryl — she's such an awful bossy-boots. Isn't old Albert, the farmhand, able to cope?

He's retired and there's only a new lad, Alec. It's just a couple of days — Dad would go, but he's working on Saturday.

So Lucy agreed to go. In her bedroom —

If I have to spend a weekend with beastly Beryl, I'll take a slice of my special loving cake —

— and if she gets too bossy, I'll use it on *HER!*

At the farm —

I don't know what use *YOU'LL* be, Lucy, but you'd better get changed quick — there's lots to do. Alec here is as thick as two planks, and doesn't move much faster either!

Poor Alec — I'd hate to work with my dear cousin around!

Go and help Alec bring in the cows for milking — and get a move on! We're late already — you should have come earlier!

I came by the first bus.

Beryl hasn't changed. She's as bossy as ever!

Lucy hurried — and slipped!

Aaaagh — yeuch!

Ha! Ha! I'd forgotten what a townie you are!

Ugh! You stink! Trust a townie not to have enough sense to walk round the edge.

It's not funny — my wellies are full of muck! You can get the cows in yourself — I'm going to change!

Later —

You'd better borrow these, they're Mum's. We'll go and move the sheep into the paddock. And don't fall into anything else! Try and be SOME help — even for a townie.

Oh, shut up, Beryl!

If she calls me a townie once more — I'll throw one of those wellies at her!

The sheep were in a big field.

Drive them over towards that corner gate. Can't you run any faster?

Phew! I seem to be doing all the running — it will keep me slim, anyway!

At last all the sheep were in the paddock.

I'm whacked! And my feet hurt — your Mum's boots are too small for me.

That's the worst of you townies. You never run — except to catch a bus. Now stop moaning about Mum's boots, and get a bale of straw for the lambing shed. I've got to go and help Mum inside for a bit —

Lucy limped over to the barn.

That's too heavy for you to carry! I'll take it.

Thank you, Alec.

What were you doing — running after the sheep? Shep can do it all right — by himself!

Shep? You mean there's a sheepdog?

So Beryl made *ME* do all that running, instead of using Shep — just to make me look a fool!

That be Brutus — the billy-goat. You stay clear of him — he butts anyone who goes near him.

Thanks for the warning, Alec — I'll watch out for him!

Later —

It's time Beryl stopped scoffing at townies. And I think my loving cake can help me to surprise her.

When no one was around, Lucy took the cake to the goat's pen —

Here's a treat for you, Brutus!

I'll try my loving cake on an *ANIMAL!* Beryl should be out again soon — I hope the cake works fast!

Lucy brought a bucket of scraps from the kitchen, just as Beryl appeared —

What a dozy lot townies are! Don't you know a bad-tempered billy-goat when you see one? *THROW* that stuff to Brutus — don't go in!

Mind your own business, Miss Know-it-all. You just don't know how to handle animals!

I *DO* hope the loving cake has worked!

Ho! Ho! Here comes Brutus — that townie's in trouble!

But —

Wh-what — ?

Hello, Brutus.

See — it all depends on how you treat him!

Well — if that don't beat all!

Uncle Dan heard about the "new" Brutus, and that afternoon —

Got anything to say about townies now, country cousin?

You were just lucky, that's all. Get back to work, Alec, and stop grinning!

You'd better tell Alec this would be a good time to move Brutus into the field, and get the pen cleaned out — while the goat's in a good mood!

THE END

On The Seashore

Try these super seashore puzzles. The answers are at the foot of the page.

SEASIDE WORD LADDER

Can you change ROCK to SAND, changing one letter at a time to make another word?

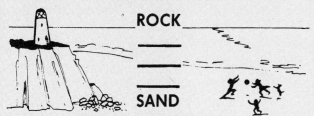

ROCK
— — — —
— — — —
SAND

THE RIDDLE OF THE SANDS

My first's found in sea and also in sail.
My second's in shark and also in whale.
My third is in sun, but never in shade.
My fourth is in dig, and it's also in spade.
My fifth's found in cove, but isn't in bay.
My sixth is in beachball, and it's in play.
My seventh's in swim, but never in float.
My eighth is in yacht, and is also in boat.
My ninth is in mussel and cockle and eel.
My tenth's found in net, and also in reel.
Complete, I am made by children for fun —
Then the sea knocks me over when each day is done!

BOAT SEARCH

Named in this square are eleven different types of boat. Can you find them? You can move up, down and diagonally — but each letter must be used once only.

R	S	T	O	O	P	E	R
E	K	I	E	L	S	N	O
A	N	K	F	A	S	C	O
T	H	S	F	E	M	E	H
N	C	B	A	G	T	R	K
U	L	T	R	R	Y	R	E
A	C	H	W	A	R	T	C
A	Y	R	E	L	E	F	H

BEACH HUNT

Follow the clues to complete the key words. We've put in some letters to help you. Then take the first letter of each completed key word. Together they will spell out a person who likes to wander on the seashore.

1. To have a dip in the sea.   _ _ T _ E
2. The tide is said to --- and flow.   _ B _
3. Used to moor a ship.   _ _ _ H _ R
4. This sea creature has sharp claws!   _ _ A _
5. The line where the sea and the sky seem to meet   _ O _ I _ O _
6. A seaside treat, filled with ice-cream.   _ O _ _ E _
7. The sea itself — a big one!   _ _ E _ _
8. He makes his living on the sea.   _ A _ I _ E _
9. A tiny, clinging sea creature!   _ _ R _ A _ _ E
10. A very slippery swimmer!   _ E _
11. In warmer places, it's made of coral.   _ E _ _

1	2	3	4	5	6	7	8	9	10	11

SCRAMBLED SEAFOOD

Can you unscramble these mixed-up words to make six different types of seafood?

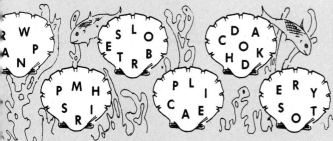

A friend for SHINING STAR

FAY CARTER was employed as a stable girl by Mr Mallory. Of all the horses in her care, Fay loved Shining Star the best, and the highlight of her day was exercising him and taking him over the jumps.

Star is in great form, soaring over the fences like a bird!

He's going to be a champion jumper, that's for sure — like his mother before him. I wish I'd worked at the stables when SHE was here.

You've worked well, Star — let's go home now, to a well-earned breakfast.

Here we are. After I've given you a good rub-down, I'll see to your feed.

Star hasn't actually worked up much of a sweat, but I'm not taking any chances. It's the County Show next week.

Star looks really magnificent. I've never seen a horse in such perfect condition. How I wish I could be the one to ride him in the show. But what's the use of dreaming? I'm just a stable girl.

Just then, Mr Mallory came in—

Here comes poor Mr Mallory! How sad he always looks, and his eyes are full of bitterness.

Star is a born winner! If only I could ride him, we'd walk away with the Championship Cup.

But the stables owner would never mount a horse again. Two years before, a tragic fall robbed him of the Championship at the last fence. He lost his best horse, and was badly injured himself.

Have you heard from your niece, sir?

Unfortunately, she's competing in Germany, so I must find another rider. I was watching you just now, and I like the way you handle Star. How would YOU like to ride him in the show?

ME? Ride Star in the show? A stable girl, competing against the best riders in the country?

It's you or no one!

With that, Mr Mallory limped away, leaving Fay in a daze of happy excitement.

Did you hear that, Star? Mr Mallory is thinking of letting me ride you in the County Show! Oh, Star — only you know how much I long to be a show-jumper, but until now it was just a hopeless dream!

But next day, as Fay was busy in the tack-room—

It's Caroline Mallory, the boss's niece! Bang goes my dream!

You, girl! Show me my uncle's best horse — the one he thinks so highly of. Come along! Shift yourself!

That's Shining Star, Miss Mallory.

Fetch his saddle, then. I'll give him a good run on the moor, to see how he reacts to discipline.

But he's been exercised already this morning. I took him over the jumps myself.

As soon as Star was tacked up, Caroline vaulted on to his back and dug her heels in. Fay opened the gate just in time—

Out of my way, girl!

Don't be impertinent, girl! If I'm to ride him in the County Show, I'll do it MY way! You are not to ride him again — understand?

There's no mistaking that Caroline is a superb horsewoman, but there's no kindness in her. Poor Star!

All morning, as Fay worked, she kept glancing towards the moor, wondering how poor Star was getting on. At last—

Oh, no! What a state he's in — shaking and sweating!

How could you ride Star so hard? He'll catch a chill, and be out of the County Show!

Don't use that tone to me! Remember your place! If you're so concerned about him, just take care of him now. That's what you're paid for!

Fay did her best for the exhausted horse—

That's better. Rest quietly now, Star. I must go and speak to Mr Mallory. Even if it costs me my job — I'll try to stop her riding you in the show.

But Fay's boss would not hear a word against his niece.

You don't know what you're saying, girl. Now that I can no longer take part in the sport, my niece is the finest show-jumper in the county. She will bring the County Cup home for me!

But—

That's enough! If you don't like it, you can leave! Well? Is that what you want?

No, sir. I could never leave Star. I love him, and he needs me.

As the days passed—

Each time Caroline rides Star she is more cruel — she's determined to master him, even if it breaks his spirit.

A hoof struck Caroline a glancing blow. She fell — and lay motionless.

Then Fay witnessed a strange sight. The riderless mare, calm now, nuzzled Star affectionately.

Well! Gentle as a lamb now — yet a moment ago, she looked like a killer!

Are you all right?

I — I think so. My head throbs, though.

That mare seemed to appear from nowhere! It was a vicious, unprovoked attack! It's lucky I wasn't killed!

Caroline swung round to point accusingly — then stared in utter amazement. Star was alone!

Wh — where is she?

She was here — I saw her! Yet there's no sign of her now! It's uncanny! She couldn't have galloped away — we can see for miles across the moor.

I'm frightened! What if she appears again? Well, I won't be here to find out what happens!

Caroline ran off towards the stables. Fay rode Star gently back, and in the yard—

Where's my niece? I thought she refused to let anyone else exercise Star.

She's gone, Mr Mallory. I saw her driving off with a suitcase.

But the County Show is tomorrow! How could Caroline let me down like this? Well, YOU'LL have to ride Star — there's nothing else for it.

Fay was delighted—

My dream has come true, Star! I WILL be a show-jumper, after all!

Fay hardly slept that night with excitement. But her nerves were well under control as she mounted Star in the show enclosure, next day—

Star's behaving perfectly, bless him. His experiences of the last week haven't affected him at all. He seems to have forgotten Caroline already.

Star jumped the first fence with ease—

Good boy!

Star soared over every fence— even the difficult water jump.

We've done it — we're in the final jump-off!

And, in the jump-off, to Fay's delight, they had the fastest clear round.

Well done, Star! Hey! Look at the boss — he's actually smiling!

And so, Fay got her first-ever trophy.

I knew Star was a winner — it's in his blood!

Later, back at the house, Mr Mallory took Fay into the library.

That's Shining Moon, Star's mother — *SHE* should have won this cup. We were leading two years ago — then she fell at the water jump, and had to be destroyed.

That painting — the crescent marking — it's the mystery horse on the moor! But — this is impossible!

And yet — is it? Shining Moon should have won two years ago — perhaps she was determined that nothing should stop her son winning *THIS* time. So her ghostly spirit returned to save him from cruel Caroline. Now Star *IS* County Champion — and, somewhere, maybe she's as proud of him as I am!

THE END

The Seasons' Spell

This poem spells out the beauty of a countryside year — and there are illustrations for YOU to colour

S Skylarks hovering in skies, their trilling notes so clear and bold —
Sticky buds and catkins, too, like streaming tassels, palest gold.

P Piglets keeping up with Mum, and squealing, *SQUEALING* as they pass!
Pony foals on unsure legs watch lapwing chicks race through the grass.

R Reeds' green shoots by riverbanks, where tadpoles swim without a rest,
Rooks in tree-top rookeries, each pair rebuilding last year's nest.

I Inky violets clustered where a mole peeps up from underground;
Ivory are the barn owl's eggs which on a feathered ledge are found.

N Nightingales with famous songs arriving for the Summer days,
Newest lambs with curly wool are frolicking in cutest ways.

G Games of boxing played by hares on hills where hawthorn blossoms white —
Growing fox cubs leave their "earth" and learn their hunting skills at night.

S Swallows skimming fresh-mown hay, and twisting honeysuckle, gold —
Sandpipers with rippling songs, by clear trout streams, so fresh and *COLD!*

U Undergrowth in cooling shade, where pretty shrews and fieldmice run;
Upstream — there the otter hunts, and swims in circles, just for fun!

M Morning haze on far-off hills, sure herald of the hottest day;
Meadows, white with daisies, where brown racing rabbits eat and play.

M Moorhens, cutting arrowed wakes amongst the waterlilies white;
Migrant birds upon a bough, against the sunset's coral light.

E Elder flowers, creamy, spiced, beneath the leafy poplars tall;
Emerald moss, like velvet, on the grey stones by a waterfall.

R Ripened corn, with flocks of birds all clamouring for yellow grain!
Rainbows, vivid after storms, and promising sunshine again.

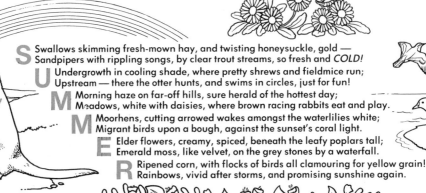

A Amber, bronze, and scarlet leaves that roll along the road to town;
Almond trees, pink blossom gone, now yield their nuts, smooth-cased and brown.

U Untamed winds shake rose-hip briars, where rambling hedges stand;
Urchins — hedgehogs — make leaf beds between tree roots, with Winter planned!

T Tractors ploughing farmland as wild geese go flying in a "V" —
Turkeys settling for the night, outdoors in a shadowed tree.

U Uplands, brown with bracken now, where plump grouse hide in heathered screen;
Unearthed potatoes in a field beyond the hawthorn hedge, still green.

M Mists and glinting moisture drops on cobwebs strung across the wood;
Mountain ash trees with red fruits that greedy birds find oh, so good!

N Newts that leave their watery home to sleep 'neath log or stone out there,
Nuts in *HOARDS* dug in the ground by squirrels — who forget just where!

W White fields, counterpaned in snow, by frozen lanes with footprints there;
Whistling winds in bulrushes — high, tossing branches, black and bare.

I Ice-bound lakes where ducks *WALK* now, as herons watch, grey-winged and grand;
Icicles on outhouse sills, and sheep in thick wool, staring bland.

N Night-time frosts that echo sounds beneath stars twinkling big and bright;
New coats for the furry stoats — from red-brown to all-over white!

T Thrushes on red-berried twigs above an icy-covered wall;
Toadstools by a fallen tree and hedgehogs rolled into a ball!

E Elm trees, dark on pearly skies, as hosts of hidden creatures sleep;
Evergreens and scented pines that dip into the snowdrifts deep.

R Rabbits gnawing tasty bark from beech trees, as their hunger grows —
Robin Redbreast on a gate, then hopping, hopping through the snows!

Angel
and the Box of Comforts

DEBBIE HUGHES lived with her parents and younger sister and brother on a council estate in London. She had recently taken on a paper round, and early one Saturday morning —

It's chilly this morning, and I'd rather be snuggled down in bed. But I want to go on the school summer cruise, and it wouldn't be right to expect Dad to find the money.

Mr Hughes, a joiner, worked for a local builder.

These days, with business being slack, Dad doesn't get the chance of any overtime — so money's short. The cruise is a luxury, and I'm determined to pay for it myself.

Later—

THE ANGELA HAMILTON MEMORIAL HOME FOR CHILDREN

Angela Hamilton was Miss Angel to the waifs of Victorian London, and that's how I think of her. A lot of books have been written about her, and I've read two of them. It's sad that her life was so short.

Miss Angel wasn't much older than I am, when she became ill and her parents were told she had only a year to live. They tried to keep the news from her, but she found out and decided to spare them the pain of a year of trying to hide their grief.

Angel had faked an accident, making it appear that she had drowned and that her body had been washed out to sea.

Angel had gone to one of the poorest areas of London, determined to devote her remaining time to helping its many needy waifs.

What courage that took! Her parents were wealthy and she'd always known every comfort. The stable she rented to house her waifs was a far cry from what she'd been used to.

Angel made the stable-house into a real home for all of them. How glad she would be to see those happy faces today, and to know that the good work is being carried on in her name.

That afternoon, Debbie wrote to her favourite uncle, a merchant seaman.

and I'm taking great care of the antique musical box you gave me at Christmas. It's beautiful! I wouldn't part with it for all the tea in China.
When will you be getting shore leave? Soon, I hope, and I expect you do, too. "Home, sweet home". Remember?
Love,
Debbie

"Home, Sweet Home" was the tune the musical box played.

Gran taught me the words — "Home, home, sweet home, There's no place like home."

Then Debbie noticed that the button on the lining of the lid was loose. As she checked it—

Oh, dear — it's come right off! And what's that hidden in the lining?

These papers must have been hidden away for years. They're thin, and brittle with age. I must handle them carefully.

Debbie began to read—

"This evening, very weary and walking slowly, I was returning to the stable-house" — the stable-house! This was written by Miss Angel!

You are ill, poor boy.

Who is it, Harry? Who's there?

Becky can't see you, miss. She's blind. It's Miss Angel, Becky. I knows it is — cos she *LOOKS* like an angel.

"Ahead I saw a boy and a girl, the boy obviously very ill. At this sight, my legs found new strength."

Are we there, Harry?

Bit further to go, Becky. The stable-house is along the lane — just stopped to get me breath back. Don't you worry now, cos I've heard that Miss Angel cares about the likes of us.

Tired — legs going —

He's got a bad chest, and a fever. Harry can't work just now, Miss Angel, so we've no money for food. Will — will you help us?

Of course I will, dear. I'm going to take you home with me, to the stable-house.

117

Towards dawn—

Annie — what is it, dear?

Miss Angel — Becky — look after — Becky — for me —

I will, Harry — I promise.

It's Harry. He can't breathe proper. I — I think he's going, Miss Angel!

Has he — has he gone, Miss Angel?

Yes, Annie. He is at peace!

Such a short life! I wish I could have saved poor Harry — if only he had come to me sooner.

Becky was heartbroken—

Harry — Harry! I wants my brother! What'll become of me now?

You'll stay with us, dear, and be one of the stable-house family. We'll care for you, and give you our love.

Angel kept a diary—

"It is two weeks now since Harry passed away. Every night Becky cries herself to sleep and, by day, she has the appearance of a sad little ghost. It is becoming increasingly difficult to persuade her to eat. Poor little Becky! My heart aches for her."

Years of deprivation have weakened her body, and now she is losing her spirit, her will to live. How can I comfort her? How?

119

How strange! I thought I felt a hand on my shoulder, and heard a voice calling my name. That voice —

It was Harry's voice! And Becky has gone!

Thank goodness she did not get far!

Becky! Becky, stay still, dear! I am coming to you!

No! No! Leave me be, Miss Angel! Let the rain and the cold finish me off! I wants to be with Harry!

No, my dear. I promised Harry I would take good care of you.

The door banging woke me up — Miss Angel! You've nothing on your feet! You'll catch your death!

But death will not catch Becky, not while there is breath in MY body!

Did — did the door banging wake you up, Miss Angel? I — I should have closed it.

It wasn't the door that wakened me, Becky. Harry still watches over you, dear, and his voice called out to me, telling me you were in danger. Not his earthly voice, Becky, but his heavenly voice — the voice of his soul. Do you understand?

122

Y — yes, I thinks I do. Harry didn't want me to die.

It'll be dreadful hard, Miss Angel. There's such an ache, here in my heart, and it just won't go away.

It will ease, dear little Becky, in time. I promise you.

That's right, dear. He loves you. He wants you to try to be happy, to try to be brave.

Drink your tea while it's hot, Miss Angel, and then off to bed with you. You looks worn out.

I am rather tired, Annie, but I have some thinking to do before I can sleep. Goodnight, Annie. God bless.

"It'll be dreadful hard," Becky said. How can I make it easier for her, quell the ache in her heart? How? Some special comfort, perhaps?

Oh! It has come to me! But have I the courage? Have I?

My comfort box. Becky has heard the children speak of it, of its power of comfort for me. She cannot see, but she could *HOLD* it, *HEAR* its sweet music.

124

125

She had such courage, such a shining spirit. Miss Angel gave up so much for her waifs.

The link with Miss Angel, the proof in her writing, will add to the value of my musical box. If I sold it — it would more than pay for the school cruise.

I shall sell it — but not for my own benefit. There are still plenty of children in need, all over the world. Angel would have wanted to help them.

Debbie went to her parents and told them of her discovery, and of the decision she had reached.

I want all the money to go to "The Save The Children Fund". I won't keep a penny of it.

Good for you, dear!

We're proud of you, Debbie.

The musical box was sold at auction, and fetched a very considerable sum. On the morning after the sale—

For you, Miss Angel.

MISS ANGEL

I wish she could know that her musical box is STILL helping children in need.

Oh! I can hear music — THE music! Is it just in my head, or —